MW00612813

ISBN: 978-1-7367281-8-5

Life can throw us all some crazy curve balls, like chemo.

One silver lining of chemo is she's predictable.

Journaling can be the best way to prepare for your treatment, so you can plan and enjoy your life. Daily journaling can make all the difference in how you live and experience your days. Even just a few sentences each day about how you're feeling can help you live a quality experience. Knowing when you'll feel good (or bad) can make it possible to plan and create memories that have nothing to do with cancer treatment and everything to do with the life and people you love.

Taking five minutes to write down things you're grateful for can change the trajectory of your day. It changed mine. It can change yours too.

Winston Churchill said, "A pessimist sees the difficulty in every opportunity. An optimist sees the opportunity in every difficulty.

"I might be a hybrid, a peptimist if you will: working hard to stay positive but secretly trying not to crap my pants."

~Carol Wyllie
Chapter 8, Chemo Pissed Me Off

May this daily journal help you embrace your faith and gratitude, and may you always sprinkle it with a little bit of attitude.

Be Well!

Carol Wyllie
Author, Chemo Pissed Me Off

Acknowledging the good you already have in your life is the foundation for all abundance.

Eckhart Tolle

Date

Date

Date

Date

Date

Date

Date

What do I have to offer today?
May I be part of His greater plan
today, whether I know it or not.

CW

Date

Date

Date

Date

Date

Date

Date

Be a seeker of knowledge.

CW

Date

Date

Date

Date
_____
_____
_____
_____
_____
_____
_____
_____
_____
_____
_____
_____
_____
_____
_____
_____
_____
_____
_____

Date

Date

Date

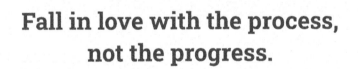

**Fall in love with the process,
not the progress.**

Date

Date

Date

Date

Date

Date

Date

**Celebrate the little things.
Every. Little. Thing.**

Date

Date

Date

Date

Date

Date

Date

Do not grieve, for the joy of the Lord is your strength.

Nehemiah 8:10

Date

Date

Date

Date

Date

Date

Date

And we know that in all things God works for the good of those who love Him, who have been called according to His purpose.

Romans 8:28

Date

Date

Date

Date

Date

Date

Date

I'm not who the world thinks
I am or even who I think I am.
I am who God says I am.

CW

Date

Date

Date

Date

Date

Date

Date

Delight yourselves in the Lord and He will give you the desires of your heart.

Psalms 37:4

Date

Date
_____

Date

Date

Date

Date
_____

Date

**You were taught to be made
new in your thinking.**

Ephesians 4:23

Date

_____
_____
_____
_____
_____
_____
_____
_____
_____
_____
_____
_____
_____
_____
_____
_____
_____
_____
_____
_____
_____

Date
_____
_____
_____
_____
_____
_____
_____
_____
_____
_____
_____
_____
_____
_____
_____
_____
_____
_____
_____
_____
_____

Date

Date

Date

Date

Date

Let the morning bring me word of your unfailing love, for I have put my trust in You. Show me the way I should go, for to You I entrust my life.

Psalms 143:8

Date

Date

Date

Date

Date

Date

Date

When I think "why me?"
may I ask instead "why not me?"
Here I am! Send me.

CW

Date

Date

Date
_____

Date

Date

Date

Date

When I don't know how to pray,
may You hear me just whisper
Your name.

Date

Date

Date

Date

Date

Date

Date

"For I know the plans I have for you," declares the Lord, "plans to prosper you and not to harm you, plans to give you hope and a future."

Jeremiah 29:11

Date

Date

Date

Date

Date

Date

Date

May I remember today all the many ways I can be grateful in my circumstances.

CW

Date

Date

Date

Date

Date

Date

Date

I will say "yes" to myself today.

CW

Date

Date

Date

Date

Date

Date

Date

I will faithfully walk into the unknown and embrace what comes next.

Date

Date

Date

Date

Date

Date

Date

As a man thinks, so he is.

Proverbs 23:7

Date

Date

Date

Date

Date

Date

Date

Words have power.
I will speak words of gratitude,
joy, and healing today.

CW

Date

Date

Date

Date

Date

Date

Date

Maybe the functionality of our lives is in direct proportion to the dysfunction we're recovering from. And that's okay.

Date

Date

Date

Date

Date

Date

Date

We are all unique.
And I am enough.

CW

Date

Date
_____
_____
_____
_____
_____
_____
_____
_____
_____
_____
_____
_____
_____
_____
_____
_____
_____
_____
_____
_____
_____
_____

Date

Date

Date

Date

Date

If you don't like something, change it. If you can't change it, change your attitude about it.

Maya Angelou

Date

Date
_____

Date

Date

Date

Date

Date

**Rejoice in the Lord always.
I will say it again: Rejoice!**

Philippians 4:4

Date

Date

Date

Date
_____
_____
_____
_____
_____
_____
_____
_____
_____
_____
_____
_____
_____
_____
_____
_____
_____
_____
_____
_____
_____
_____
_____

Date

Date

Date

God does not comfort us to make us comfortable, but to make us comforters.

Billy Graham

Date

Date

Date

Date

Date

Date

Date

I am living proof that God can
take the most unlikely candidates
and circumstances and turn them
into something beautiful.

CW

Date

Date

Date

Date

Date

Date

Date

Made in the USA
Coppell, TX
13 November 2022

86310851R00116